What am I?

Look at each picture, then read the senten
Draw a line to the sentence that tells you what each pi...... is.

I hold water.

I cut things.

I paint pictures.

I tell the time.

I send e-mails.

The street

Look at the street.
Which house number has:

no curtains at the windows? _____

an open gate? _____

a cat in the window? _____

an apple tree? _____

smoke coming from its chimney? _____

a Christmas tree? _____

a big van outside? _____

a car outside? _____

its number on the gate? _____

What are they?

Join the **fish** to the bowl. Colour the **fish** orange.
Join the **birds** to the bird table. Colour the **birds** blue.
Write the words under the pictures.

stingray

goldfish

owl

seahorse

birds

flamingo

fish

robin

duck

shark

5

Who said it?

Look at the pictures.
Read each sentence.
Draw a line from the animal you think might have said it.

I like going
for walks.

I give
children rides.

I lay eggs.

I live in
the sea.

I catch mice.

6

Right or wrong!

Look at the pictures. Read the sentences. Decide whether the sentence is correct or not, then circle **yes** or **no**.

It is a windy day.   yes   no

The cat is afraid of the dog.   yes   no

Mum washed two T-shirts.   yes   no

The eggs are about to hatch.   yes   no

The children walk to school.   yes   no

Ashi bought some flowers.   yes   no

Liam ate an apple.   yes   no

Toby ironed his shirt.   yes   no

What's next?

Look at the pictures.
Read the sentences and then tick the box that tells the story.

Jake has 50p.
He likes ice-cream.

 or

Amy fell off her bike.
She hurt her knee.

 or

Matt has brushed
his teeth.

 or

In the garden

Read the sentences.
Follow the instructions.

     Colour the frog green.
     Draw a yellow flower between the two flowers.
     Draw two ducks.
     Draw a big kite in the sky.
     Put ten red apples on the tree.
     Draw four goldfish in the pond.

Animal riddles

Draw a ring round the correct animal.

I am pink.
I have a curly tail.
I grunt.

I hoot.
I have big eyes.
I fly in the dark.

I am red.
I have spots.
I have six legs.

I have fur.
I have long ears.
I like carrots.

What are they?

Join the **trees** to the wood. Colour the **trees** green.
Join the **flowers** to the vase. Colour the **flowers** yellow.
Write the words under the pictures.

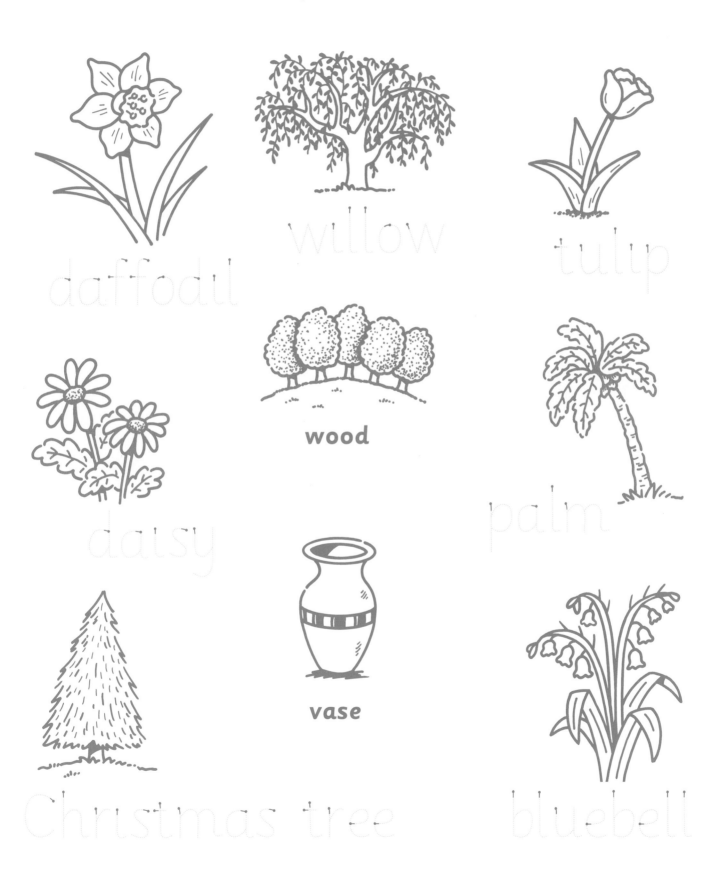

daffodil

willow

tulip

wood

daisy

palm

Christmas tree

vase

bluebell

What is happening?

Look at each picture, then read the sentences.
Draw a line to the sentence that tells you about each picture.

The frog is on
the lily-pad.

Lucy likes ice-cream.

The robin is
on her nest.

The jelly has set.

Gary has scored a goal.

What does it mean?

The pictures tell you what is happening.
Circle the words that tell you what each picture means.

No dogs allowed.
We do not like pets.

Sports Day is on Monday.
No children at Sports Day.

We sell hens.
We sell eggs.

Children crossing.
Do not cross here.

The bus stops here.
The train stops here.

What else goes here?

Draw something else that can go in each group.
Choose the correct group name and then write it on the line.

t r

_____

_____

_____

| fish | trees | minibeasts | birds |

What am I?

Draw a ring round the correct toy.

I am soft and cuddly.
My name is Ted.

You can blow me up!
I can go POP!

You can bang me!
I make a loud noise.

I can roll.
You can catch me.

At the seaside

Read the sentences.
Follow the instructions.

- Draw and colour the sun above the clouds.
- Draw a bird in the sky.
- Colour the sails red and put a number on one of them.
- Colour the starfish orange.
- Draw yourself on the beach.

What else goes here?

Draw something else that can go in each group.
Choose the correct group name and then write it on the line.

shoes   flags   hats   glasses

What's next?

Look at the picture.
Read the sentence and then tick in the box that tells the story.

Anna likes to fly her kite.

Mark goes skiing.

Tara bought some
flowers.

Why?

Look at the pictures.
Read the sentences, then colour the box ☐ next to the reason why.

The seal dived in the water
☐ to go to sleep.
☐ to catch a fish.

The spider spun a web because
☐ he wanted to catch a fly.
☐ he was lost.

The dog went to the vet because
☐ he was ill.
☐ he saw a cat.

The frog sat on his lily pad because
☐ he was watching a fish.
☐ he was tired

The penguin walked in the snow because
☐ he couldn't fly.
☐ he was in a hurry.

Canal side

Read the sentences.
Follow the instructions.

Colour the boat blue.
Draw smoke coming from the boat's funnel.
Draw two people on the boat.
Write the boat's name in the box.
Draw the fish the boy caught.

Match the books

Draw a line to join each book to its cover.

The wizard cast his spell.

Penguins cannot fly.

Clowns make us laugh.

Cows give us milk.

Racing cars are fast.

Animals from Cold Lands

On the Farm

MAGIC

SPEED

The Circus

21

What's the idea?

Look at the pictures then read the sentences in the speech bubbles.
Colour the square next to the sentence that tells the main idea.

☐ The penguin is hungry.
☐ The penguin has eaten too much.

☐ The cake is too small.
☐ Today is Sam's birthday.

☐ The dog has lost his bone.
☐ The dog wants another bone.

☐ The squirrel is planting acorns.
☐ The squirrel is hiding acorns.

☐ Nisha hates her scooter.
☐ Nisha enjoys riding her scooter.

At home

Read the sentences.
Follow the instructions.

Draw a door in the house. Colour it red.
Give it a number between 2 and 8.
Draw two windows downstairs and three windows upstairs.
Draw a path to the door.

 **THINK!** *What can you see in the windows?*

Put in order!

Look at each picture. Read the words.
Write 1, 2 and 3 in the boxes so that the words are in the
correct order to tell a story.

2 dry
1 wash
3 iron

☐ eat
☐ peel
☐ fry

☐ flour
☐ loaf
☐ wheat

☐ honey
☐ bees
☐ flowers

☐ fire
☐ 999
☐ fireman

☐ water
☐ slide
☐ climb

Why?

Look at the pictures.
Read the sentences, then colour the box ☐ next to the reason why.

Ellen went to the library because
☐ she wanted a book to read.
☐ she wanted an ice-cream.

Patrick fed the birds because
☐ he was hungry.
☐ it was winter.

Laura had a disco because
☐ her cat was lost.
☐ it was her birthday.

The snowman melted because
☐ the sun shone.
☐ it was cold.

Tristan dug in the sand because
☐ the fish swam away.
☐ he was at the seaside.

Camping

Read the sentences.
Follow the instructions.

Colour the tent yellow.
Draw two more tents.
Colour one tent green and the other tent orange.
Draw a tree and colour it.
Draw the sun and two clouds.

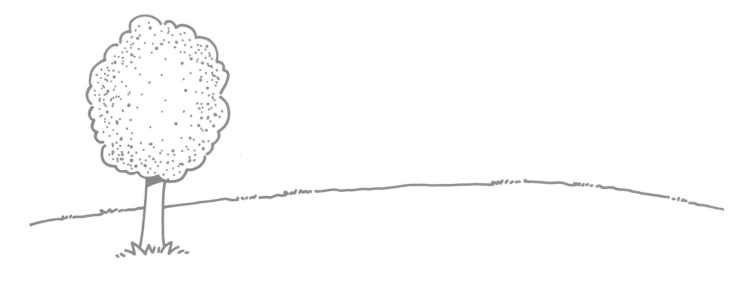

Put in order!

Look at each picture. Read the words.
Write 1, 2 and 3 in the boxes so that the words are in the
correct order to tell a story.

3 land	
1 take off	
2 fly	

☐ answer	
☐ ring	
☐ listen	

☐ frog	
☐ spawn	
☐ tadpoles	

☐ open	
☐ give	
☐ buy	

☐ pick	
☐ grow	
☐ plant	

☐ melt	
☐ snowman	
☐ sunshine	

Fairy stories

Look at the covers of these books.

Write the titles of the
Fairy Tales.

_____

_____

_____

Write the titles of the other
stories.

_____

_____

_____

Who is the author of
Monsters on the Moon?

_____

Draw a cover on this book
for Little Red Riding Hood.

What kind of story is it?

_____

_____

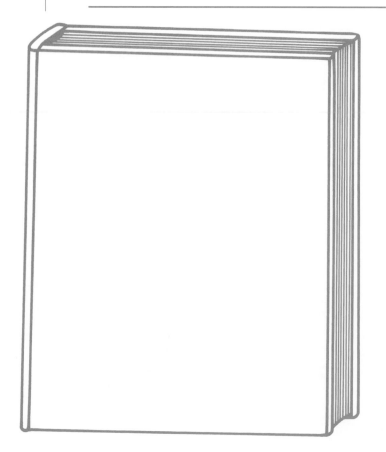

Put in order!

Look at each picture. Read the words.
Write 1, 2 and 3 in the boxes so that the words are in the
correct order to tell a story.

3 turn off
2 watch
1 turn on

☐ eat
☐ crack
☐ boil

☐ close
☐ read
☐ open

☐ bake
☐ mix
☐ eat

☐ land
☐ lift off!
☐ orbit

☐ wash
☐ eat
☐ pick

Why?

Look at the pictures.
Read the sentences, then colour the box ☐ next to the reason why.

Jane had sunglasses because
☐ the sun was shining.
☐ it was raining.

Harry is cheering because
☐ his team lost the match.
☐ his team won the cup.

The cat ran away because
☐ the dog chased her.
☐ she wanted some fish.

Martin laughed because
☐ Dad put his foot in the paint can.
☐ Dad painted the door.

Mum's hat blew off because
☐ it was too big.
☐ the wind was blowing.

Nursery rhymes

Look at the covers of these books.

Write the titles of the
Nursery Rhyme Books.

_____

_____

_____

Write the titles of the
Poetry Books.

_____

_____

_____

Draw a cover on the book for this Nursery Rhyme.

Little Boy Blue,
Come blow your horn,
The sheep's in the meadow,
The cow's in the corn.

Give this book a title.

_____

Which is your favourite

Nursery Rhyme?

_____

Schofield&Sims

the long-established educational publisher
specialising in maths, English and science materials for schools

Early Comprehension is a series of graded activity books that develop children's ability to make sense of pictures and text – through activities such as story sequencing, reading for meaning and traditional comprehension work.

Early Comprehension Book 2 covers:

- matching pictures with captions
- reading simple instructions
- riddles
- speech bubbles.

The full range of titles in the series is as follows:

Early Comprehension Book 1:   ISBN 978 07217 0917 8

Early Comprehension Book 2:   ISBN 978 07217 0918 5

Early Comprehension Book 3:   ISBN 978 07217 0950 5

Have you tried **Pre-reading Skills** by Schofield & Sims?
In this series, **Scamp the dog** helps children to make sense of print by looking at picture cues and by sequencing stories.

**For further information and to place your order
visit www.schofieldandsims.co.uk or telephone 01484 607080**

First edition copyright © Schofield and Sims Ltd, 2003
Sixth impression 2010
Authors: Anne Forster and Paul Martin

Printed in the UK by Wyndeham Gait Ltd, Grimsby, Lincolnshire

ISBN 978-07217-0918-5

ISBN 978 07217 0918 5

9 780721 709185

Schofield&Sims

Dogley Mill, Fenay Bridge, Huddersfield HD8 0NQ
Phone: 01484 607080 Facsimile: 01484 606815
E-mail: sales@schofieldandsims.co.uk

**£2.45
(Retail price)**

Key Stage 1
Age range: 5–7 years

MUSIC WORKOUT

Grade 2

Jean Archibald   Bernadette Marmion

Royal Irish Academy of Music

GRADE 2

Syllabus

Note / Rest Values	Note values of semibreve to semiquaver inclusive. Dotted notes and tied notes. Rest values of semibreve to quaver inclusive.
Time	Grouping of notes and rests in $\frac{2}{4}$, $\frac{3}{4}$ and $\frac{4}{4}$.
Stave	Notes to the second ledger space above and below Treble and Bass.
Signs	The writing and use of sharp, flat and natural signs.
Scales	Major scales, key signatures and tonic triads of C, G, D and F. Their application in (a) recognising the key of a piece; (b) adding accidentals instead of a key signature; (c) using relevant tonic solfa.
Observation	Observation of the above elements in answering simple questions about a melody, including more terms and signs.

A Note to the Teacher

The sight singing exercises are introduced by using Stick Notation ; this shows the solfa names and the rhythm. Hand signs are used as a visual aid to pitch. Reading from the stave is encouraged ; this is facilitated by the use of a ' *do* clef ': **C**. *do* may be pitched on any note to suit the student's range.

Text Signals

● indicates where new concepts and information are introduced.

■ indicates points to be memorised and useful hints.

First published in 1998 by
The Royal Irish Academy of Music
Westland Row, Dublin 2.

©1998 by The Royal Irish Academy of Music

ISBN 1 - 902140 - 03 - 6

Music processing   Jean Archibald and Bernadette Marmion
Typesetting and graphics   Creighton Music, Dublin 14.
Cover design   Origin Design Associates.
Printed by   Brunswick Press, Dublin 12.

CONTENTS

PART 1

REVISION of LETTER NAMES and TIME NAMES

Exercise 1 Underneath each note write its letter name, its time name and how many beats it lasts for. The first one has been started as a guide.

a)

letter name :   G   ____   ____   ____   ____

time name :   Minim   _____   _____   _____   _____

number of beats : __2__   ____   ____   ____   ____

b)

letter name :   ____   ____   ____   ____   ____

time name :   _____   _____   _____   _____   _____

number of beats : ____   ____   ____   ____   ____

c)

letter name :   ____   ____   ____   ____   ____

time name :   _____   _____   _____   _____   _____

number of beats : ____   ____   ____   ____   ____

d)

letter name :   ____   ____   ____   ____   ____

time name :   _____   _____   _____   _____   _____

number of beats : ____   ____   ____   ____   ____

e)

letter name :   ____   ____   ____   ____   ____

time name :   _____   _____   _____   _____   _____

number of beats : ____   ____   ____   ____   ____

f)

letter name: ____   ____   ____   ____   ____

time name :   _____   _____   _____   _____   _____

number of beats : ____   ____   ____   ____   ____

THE SEMIQUAVER

● The word **semi** means ' half '. For example, semicircle means half a circle; semitone means half a tone. So **semiquaver** means half a quaver.

A semiquaver looks like this ♬ or ♬ . Its other name is **sixteenth note**.

Study these drawings to see the different notes as divisions of the semibreve.

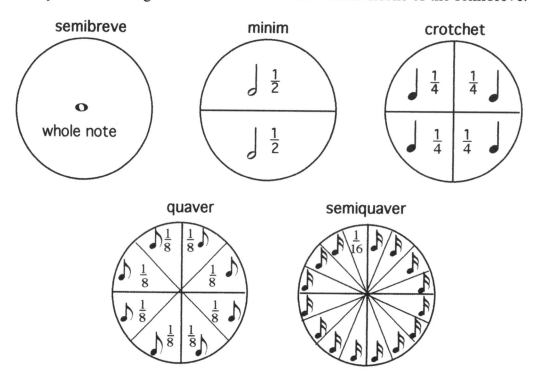

The following pyramid chart shows all the note values learnt so far.

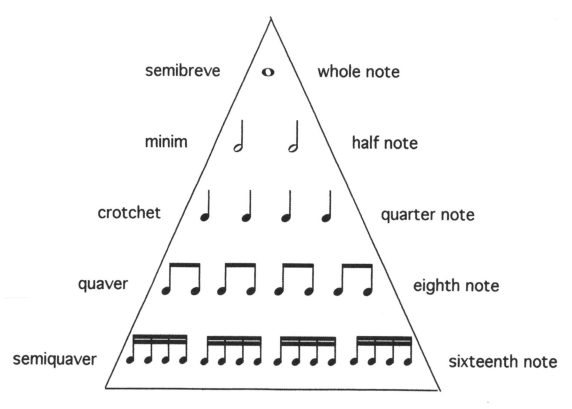

3 EXERCISES with SEMIQUAVERS

Two semiquavers equal the value of a quaver. ♫ = ♪

Four semiquavers equal the value of a crotchet. ♬♬ = ♩

A mixture of semiquavers and quavers can be joined in one group like this : ♫♪ and ♪♫

Exercise 2 After each group write <u>one</u> note which will show the total value of the group.

a)

b)

Exercise 3 Add the missing bar lines in the following rhythms.

a)

b)

c)

d)

e)

f)

SIGHT CLAPPING 1

●   This is a table of the rhythm patterns used in the next group of clapping exercises. Crotchets, quavers and semiquavers are used.

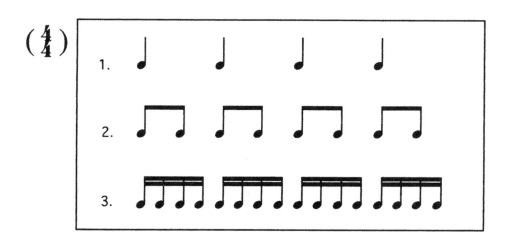

Exercise 4 Practise clapping the rhythms in the table several times. Sometimes change the order. Count aloud to help you keep a steady beat.

Exercise 5 Clap each of the following rhythms while keeping an even beat.

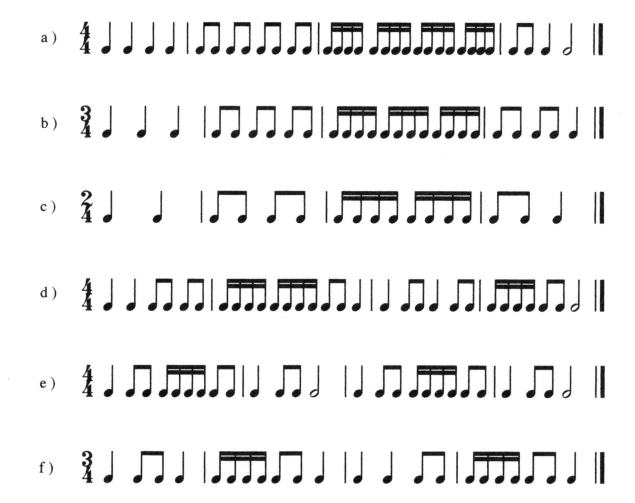

LEDGER LINES and SPACES : TREBLE

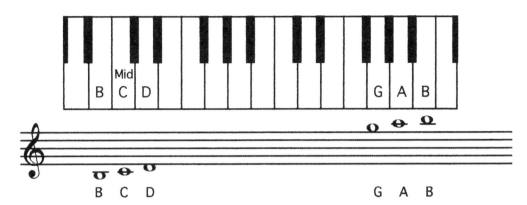

You already know D and C <u>below</u> the treble stave. Now B is added; it is on the second ledger space below the treble stave. Looking at the notes <u>above</u> the treble stave, you already know G and A. Now B is added on the second ledger space above the treble stave.

Think of the ledger lines as an extension of the stave, so when you draw them, keep the distance between ledger lines the same as the distance between the stave lines.

As notes move further away from the stave on ledger lines and spaces, all ledger lines <u>between</u> the stave and the note must be drawn. But no ledger line beyond the note is needed.

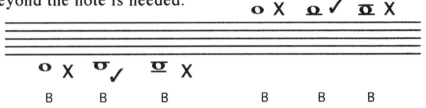

Exercise 6 Practise drawing notes in ledger lines and spaces by copying these notes in the blank bars.

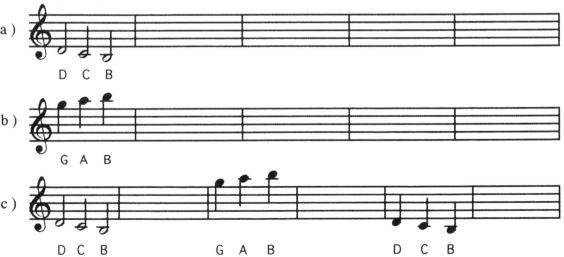

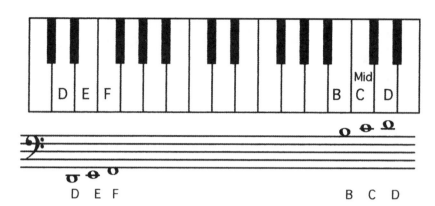

You already know F and E <u>below</u> the bass stave. Now D is added ; it is
the second ledger space below the bass stave. Looking at the notes <u>above</u>
the bass stave, you already know B and C. Now D is added on the second
ledger space above the bass stave.

Exercise 7 Practise drawing the notes in the ledger lines and spaces by copying these
notes in the blank bars.

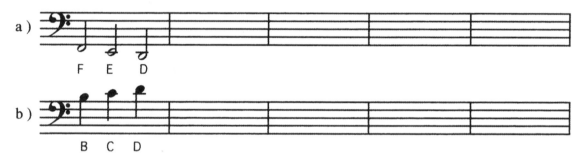

The treble and bass staves are separated by only one line - the Middle C
line. It is shown below as a broken line because it is always used as a
ledger line. It is easy to see how B, Middle C and D can be written two
ways : either below the treble or above the bass. They sound the same
whichever way you write them.

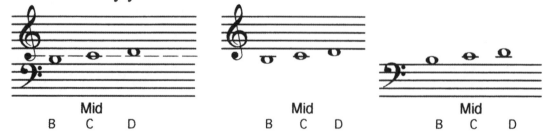

Exercise 8 Practise drawing B, Middle C and D below the treble stave and above the
bass stave.

EXERCISES on LEDGER LINES and SPACES

Exercise 9 Write the letter name below each note.

Exercise 10 Give the letter name of each of the following notes. Then using ledger lines or spaces <u>above</u> the stave, draw another note with the same letter name.

Exercise 11 Give the letter name of each of the following notes. Then using ledger lines or spaces <u>below</u> the stave, draw another note with the same letter name.

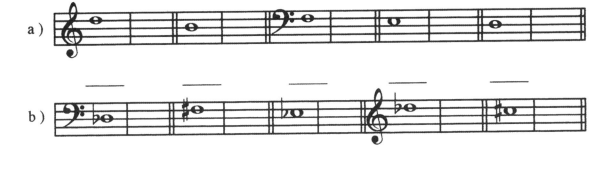

Exercise 12 Name each note.

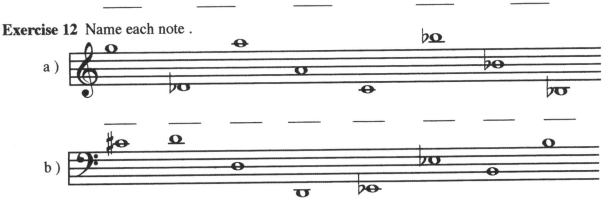

THE NATURAL SIGN

A **natural** sign ♮ is used to cancel a sharp or flat sign. Like sharp and flat signs it must be written <u>on the same line or space</u> as the note to which it belongs.

G sharp   G natural   B flat   B natural

Exercise 13   Cancel the sharp or flat by drawing a natural before the second note of each pair.

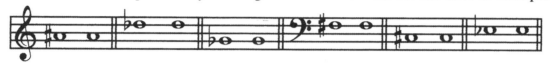

Exercise 14   Write the letter name under each note, and draw a circle around the <u>higher</u> note of each pair.

a)

b)

c)

Exercise 15   Write the letter name under each note, and draw a circle around the <u>lower</u> note of each pair.

a)

b)

Exercise 16   Re-write each note to make it a semitone <u>higher</u>.

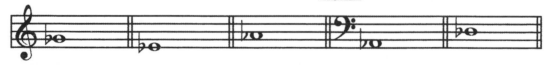

Exercise 17   Rewrite each note to make it a semitone <u>lower</u>.

• Do you remember the notes you learned to sing in previous grades? They were *d* , *r* , *m* and *s* .

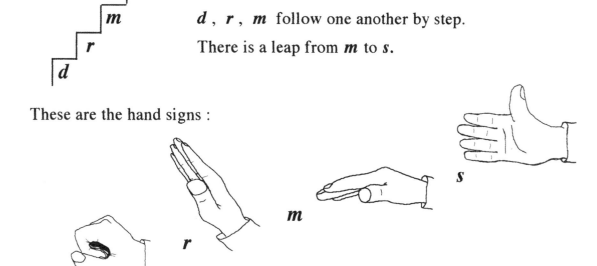

d , *r* , *m* follow one another by step.

There is a leap from *m* to *s*.

These are the hand signs :

The sign **C** shows the position of *do*. It may be on any line or space.

For example :

We also sang tunes written in the key of C major and G major. Now try to sing these tunes with tonic solfa names.

Exercise 18 Sing this tune using solfa names. Keep an even beat by tapping your hand or foot.

Now write the tune on the stave. **C** shows where *d* will be. When you have finished writing, sing the tune again. This time make the hand signs as you sing.

This group of tunes uses *d* , *r* , *m* and *s*. Now quavers are added to the rhythm.

Exercise 19 Sing each of these tunes using tonic solfa names. Keep an even beat by quietly tapping your hand or foot.

Exercise 20 In the next melody one bar has been left out. Sing the part of the melody which is given. Then compose your own missing bar, writing in the notes and the rhythm. When you have done this, sing the whole melody.

MUSICAL TERMS and SIGNS

● This page provides a review of the musical terms and signs you learned in Grade 1 and introduces some new ones. The new terms for Grade 2 are printed in bold type.

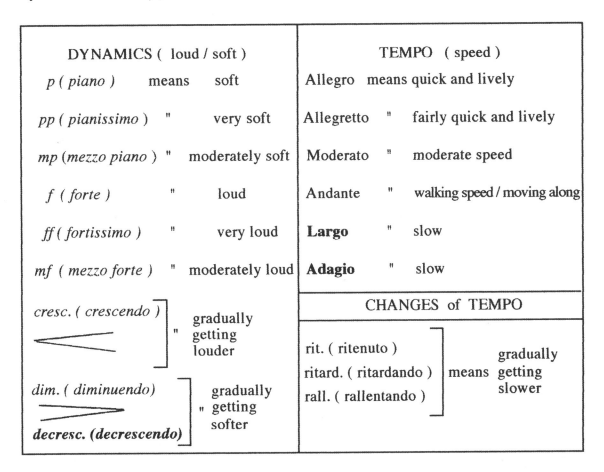

DYNAMICS (loud / soft)			TEMPO (speed)		
p (piano)	means	soft	Allegro	means	quick and lively
pp (pianissimo)	"	very soft	Allegretto	"	fairly quick and lively
mp (mezzo piano)	"	moderately soft	Moderato	"	moderate speed
f (forte)	"	loud	Andante	"	walking speed / moving along
ff (fortissimo)	"	very loud	**Largo**	"	slow
mf (mezzo forte)	"	moderately loud	**Adagio**	"	slow

cresc. (crescendo) 〈 " gradually getting louder

dim. (diminuendo) 〉 " gradually getting softer
decresc. (decrescendo)

CHANGES of TEMPO

rit. (ritenuto)
ritard. (ritardando) 〉 means gradually getting slower
rall. (rallentando)

Exercise 21 Add these terms and signs to this piece of music " *Eileen Aroon* ".

a) A word above bar 1 which means ' walking speed '.

b) Letters below bar 1 which mean ' play moderately softly '.

c) A sign below bar 2 which means ' get gradually louder '.

d) A sign below bars 3 and 4 which means ' get gradually softer '.

e) A letter below bar 5 which means ' play softly '.

f) Letters below bar 9 which mean ' play moderately loud '.

g) A letter below bar 13 which means ' play loudly '.

h) A word above bar 15 which means ' get gradually slower '.

This piece is the right-hand part of the opening of a *'Gavotte'* by Handel. Study the music. Then answer the questions below.

a) Explain the meaning of these musical terms and signs.

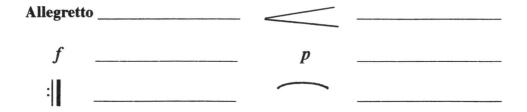

Allegretto _____   ◁◁◁ _____

f _____   *p* _____

:‖ _____   ◠ _____

b) Answer the following :

   (i) Is the music written in the key of C major or G major ? _____

   (ii) Write the time signature as two numbers. _____

   (iii) The letter name of the highest note is _____ . Its solfa name is _____ .

   (iv) The letter name of the lowest note is _____ . Its solfa name is _____ .

   (v) The first phrase is marked ┌───┐ . Mark in the same way where this phrase is heard again.

c) To answer these questions, tick the box with the correct answer.

   (i) How many times is F♯ heard ?   ☐ 5   ☐ 6   ☐ 7

   (ii) Which bar sounds G for three beats ?   ☐ 2   ☐ 3   ☐ 4

   (iii) Which bar has the most repeated notes ?   ☐ 2   ☐ 3   ☐ 4

   (iv) On which note does the tune begin ?   ☐ *d*   ☐ *r*   ☐ *m*

   (v) On which note does the tune end ?   ☐ *d*   ☐ *m*   ☐ *s*

Q. 1   Write both names for each note and rest. The first one is already done as a guide.

dotted minim   _____ _____ _____ _____

dotted half-note   _____ _____ _____ _____

Q. 2   Add the barlines to this rhythm.

Q.3   Name each note.

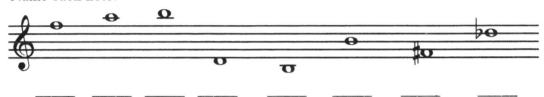

____ ____ ____ ____ ____ ____ ____

Q.4 a)What sign is used to cancel a sharp or flat sign ? _____

   b)Draw each note with its sign on the stave. Mark with X the higher note of each pair.

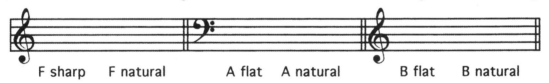

   F sharp   F natural   A flat   A natural   B flat   B natural

Q.5   Write one note (dotted if necessary) where you see * , to complete each bar.

Q.6   Explain in your own words :

Adagio _____ *rit.* _____ **Andante** _____

decrescendo _____ *mp* _____ **Lento** _____

Q.7   Write this tune on the stave. ⟨ shows where *d* will be.

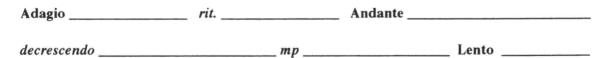

   d   d   r   r   m   s   m   m   r   d   r   m   s   d

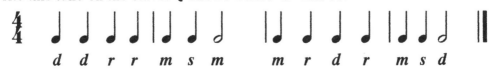

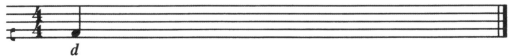

   d

THE QUAVER REST

●   For a silent half beat a **quaver rest** is used. The quaver rest is written like this ⅄

Exercise 22 Practise drawing a single quaver followed by a quaver rest to fill this stave.

Exercise 23 Add the missing bar lines in the following rhythms.

Exercise 24 Add one rest at each place marked * to make the bar complete.

SIGHT CLAPPING 2

• In these clapping exercises ♩. ♪ is combined with ♩ ♩ and ♫♫

This is a table of the rhythm patterns used in the next group of clapping exercises.

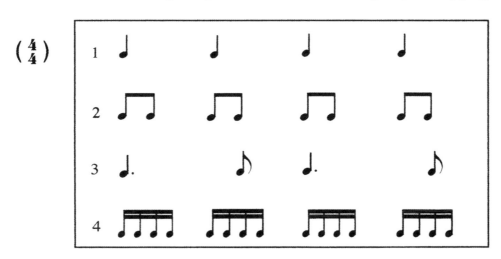

Exercise 25 Practise clapping the rhythms in the table several times. Sometimes change the order. Count aloud to help you keep a steady beat.

Exercise 26 Clap each of the following rhythms while keeping an even beat.

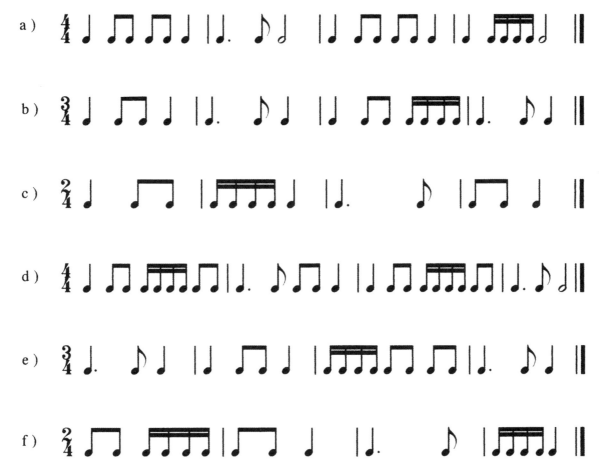

Exercise 27 Write the letter name under each note.

Exercise 28 Draw either the treble (G) or bass (F) clef before each of these notes to make its letter name correct.

a) C   B flat   F sharp   A   D flat   F

b) E   G sharp   A flat   D   D flat   B

c) D flat   D flat   F sharp   C   B   D sharp

d) E flat   A sharp   D sharp   G flat   D sharp   C

Exercise 29 Draw each note above or below the stave using ledger lines or spaces.

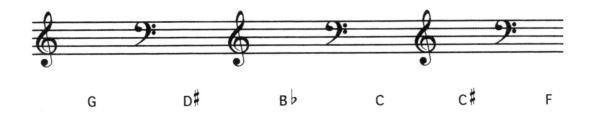

G   D♯   B♭   C   C♯   F

**EXERCISES on TONES and SEMITONES
REVISION of SCALES C and G**

Exercise 30 Give the letter name of each note. Then draw another note one semitone <u>higher</u>.

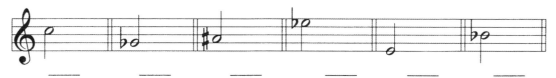

Exercise 31 Give the letter name of each note. Then draw another note one semitone <u>lower</u>.

Exercise 32 Give the letter names of these notes. Describe the distance between each pair
of notes as <u>tone</u> or <u>semitone</u> by writing **T** or **S** in the box above.

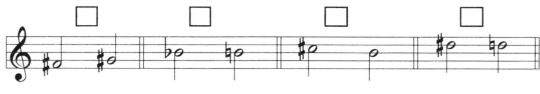

● In Grade 1 you learned to write the scales of C and G. Do you remember the
pattern of tones and semitones needed to make a major scale? Here it is again.

d   r   m   f   s   l   t   d'
tone   tone semitone tone   tone tone semitone

This is the scale of C ascending.   And the scale of C descending.

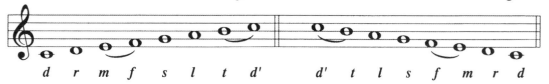

d   r   m   f   s   l   t   d'   d'   t   l   s   f   m   r   d

This is the scale of G written : (a) with an accidental; (b) with a key signature.

d   r   m   f   s   l   t   d'   d   r   m   f   s   l   t   d'

Exercise 33 Complete the scales by following the instructions given for each.

a) Add the clef to make this the scale of
C major. Give solfa names. Mark semitones.

b) Add the accidental to make this the scale of
G major. Give solfa names. Mark semitones.

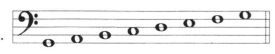

●   An accidental affects a note on the same line or space for the rest of the bar.

still F♯

An accidental will not affect a note with the same letter name at a different pitch, so it needs to be written again.

♯ needs to be written again.

An accidental carries into the next bar on a tied note and is not written again. Tied notes are explained more fully on page 25 ; for now, you just need to know that the 2nd note is not <u>played</u> again.

still F♯ because it is tied.

Exercise 34 Below each note marked * tick the box which correctly names it.

SINGING with SOLFA 3 : ADDING *l*

● In this group of tunes a new note *la* (*l*) is added. It is a step higher than *so* .

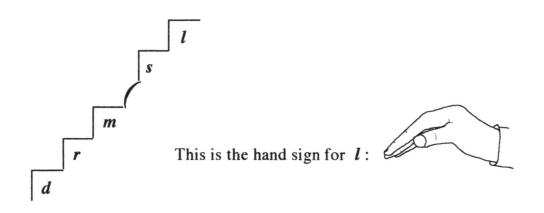

This is the hand sign for *l* :

Exercise 35 Sing each of these tunes using tonic solfa names. Keep an even beat by tapping quietly with your hand or foot.

a) $\frac{4}{4}$
d r m r m s s   s l s m r r d

b) $\frac{3}{4}$
d r m s   l   s m r d

c) $\frac{2}{4}$
d m s s l l s   s l s m r r d

d) $\frac{3}{4}$
d r m s l s   s l s m d

e) $\frac{4}{4}$
d r m r d r r m   s l s m r d r d

f) $\frac{2}{4}$
d m s l s m r m   s l s m r d r d

Exercise 36 Finish the tune by composing your own missing bar. When you have finished writing, sing the complete tune.

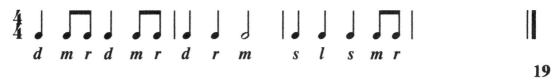

$\frac{4}{4}$
d m r d m r d r m   s l s m r

● Here are *d* , *r* , *m* , *s* and *l* in different positions on the stave.

Here they are again in the keys of C major and G major.

Exercise 37 Sing each tune using tonic solfa names. Keep a steady beat while doing so.

Exercise 38 (a) Complete the tune by composing your own missing bar. When you have
finished writing, sing the tune.

(b) Now write the completed tune on the stave in the key of C major.
To start you off, the first few notes are already written in.

● **Tempo** and **Changes of Tempo**   The <u>speed</u> at which a piece is to be played is shown by a word such as **Allegro** or **Largo**. A sign may be used: M.M. ♩= 60. This means 60 crotchet beats per minute. It is called a **metronome marking**. Each ' tick ' of the metronome is the length of a beat. Metronome markings of pieces vary as composers decide, e.g. M.M.♩ = 80 ; M.M.♩ = 88 ; etc.

Other terms to do with tempo are the following :

poco rall. ⎤
poco rit. ⎦ = gradually getting a little slower.

accelerando = gradually getting faster.
a tempo = back to normal speed.

● **Articulation**   The <u>touch</u> that a performer uses when playing music on an instrument is called **articulation**. Two of the most usual types are :

Legato meaning <u>smooth playing</u> and usually shown by a slur.

Staccato meaning <u>detached</u> playing. It is shown by a dot under or over the notes.

● **Style**   Sometimes the music needs to be played in a certain style. This is shown by **style markings**, e.g. :

dolce   play sweetly.
cantabile   play in a singing style.

grazioso   play gracefully.

● **Musical signs**

⌢̣ = pause. Stay a little longer on the marked note.

> = accent. Emphasise the marked note.

— = stress. Lean. Give fuller tone to the marked note.

8ᵛᵃ – – – – – – , The sign is placed above notes which are to be played one octave higher.

8ᵛᵇ – – – – – – ˌ The sign is placed below notes which are to be played one octave lower.

Repeat marks   ⫶‖ = Repeat from beginning.   ‖⫶   ⫶‖ = Repeat section between dots.

⫶‖⫶ = Repeat the sections <u>before and after</u> the sign.

This sign is used when a composer wants to use two different endings for a repeated section. When the section is played the first time only bar ⎾1 is played. When the section is played a second time only bar ⎾2 is played. If the performer decides not to repeat, then only bar ⎾2 will be played.

GENERAL OBSERVATION 2

This is the right-hand part of a piano piece '*Melody*' by Schumann. Study the music. Then answer the questions below.

a) Explain the meaning of these musical terms and signs.

Moderato _____

$\text{♩} = 116$ _____

p _____

b) i) Is the music written in the key of C major or G major ? _____

ii) Show another way to write the time signature. _____

iii) Give the letter name of the highest note. _____ Its solfa name is _____ .

iv) Give the letter name of the lowest note. _____ Its solfa name is _____ .

v) Use ⌐‾‾ to mark the two notes where the widest jump occurs.

c) Tick the box to show whether the sentence is 'true' or 'false'.

i) $\frac{4}{4}$ time is the same as Common Time. | true | false |

ii) When played with repeats the melody is 16 bars long. | true | false |

iii) The first two bars are repeated immediately. | true | false |

iv) The first two bars are repeated later. | true | false |

v) The longest note used is a dotted crotchet. | true | false |

23

Q.1 Draw the missing bar lines in this rhythm.

Q. 2 Add one rest at each place marked * to make the bar complete.

Q. 3 Draw the named note. After each note draw another which is a semitone <u>higher</u>.

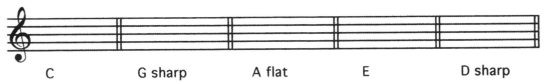

     C   G sharp   A flat   E   D sharp

Q. 4 (a) Add a clef and key signature to make these notes form the scale of G major.

(b) Write the scale of C major ascending in minims. Add solfa names; mark semitones.

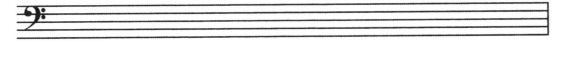

Q. 5 How many times is F sharp played in the following tune? _____

Q. 6 Add the following terms and signs to the music.

a) A tempo mark above bar 1 to show that the music is played fairly lively.

b) Signs in bars 1 and 3 to show that the notes are played *staccato*.

c) A sign in bars 2 and 4 to show that the notes are played smoothly.

d) A sign above the last two bars to show that they are played one octave higher.

e) A sign in the last bar to show that the piece is played again.

f) Two words in the last bar to show that the music gradually gets a little slower.

PART 3
THE DOTTED QUAVER

● You have already learnt that a dot after a note makes the sound longer by half as much again. The table below shows the values of dotted notes. It includes the dotted quaver.

> Remember the dot is always worth half the value of its note.
>
> 𝗈· is the same as 𝗈 + ♩ together in one sound.
>
> ♩· is the same as ♩ + ♩ together in one sound.
>
> ♩· is the same as ♩ + ♪ together in one sound.
>
> ♪· is the same as ♪ + ♬ together in one sound

Exercise 39 Draw a note to show the value of each dot for the following :

♩. = ♩ + ___   ♪. = ♪ + ___

♩. = ♩ + ___   𝗈· = 𝗈 + ___

Exercise 40 After each group write <u>one dotted note</u> which shows the total value of the group.

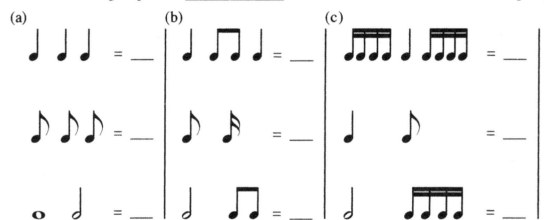

Exercise 41 Add <u>one note</u>, dotted if necessary, at each place marked * to complete the bar.

TIED NOTES

● A **tie** is another way of making a longer sound. A tie is a curved line which looks like this ⌒ Notes which follow one another on the <u>same line or space</u> may be tied. The curved line is drawn on the outer side of the noteheads. It joins the value of the notes together in one longer sound:

For example, 𝅗𝅥‿𝅘𝅥 makes one sound lasting for 3 crotchet beats.

𝅝‿𝅘𝅥 makes one sound lasting for 5 crotchet beats.

𝅗𝅥‿𝅘𝅥‿𝅘𝅥𝅮 makes one sound lasting for $3\frac{1}{2}$ crotchet beats.

A tie is used when a sound is held over a bar line and when a dot is not suitable.

Exercise 42 Draw X at every place where a tie is used. Write the number of crotchet beats for which each tied sound will last. The first one is done as a guide.

2 beats

Exercise 43 Add a tie wherever possible in the following melodies. Below the tie, write the number of crotchet beats for which each tied sound will last.

In these clapping exercises ⁷ is combined with ♫ 𝄢 and ♩. ♪
The different combinations are shown below.

Exercise 44 Practise clapping the rhythms in the table several times. Sometimes change the order. Count aloud to help you keep a steady beat.

Exercise 45 Clap each of the following rhythms while keeping a steady beat.

GROUPING NOTES

You will have noticed that notes such as quavers and semiquavers are usually joined (**beamed**) in groups. In $\frac{2}{4}$, $\frac{3}{4}$ and $\frac{4}{4}$ times these shorter notes are grouped (beamed) into crotchet beats. This helps the reading and counting of the rhythm.

To learn to group notes correctly, study the points made in this table :

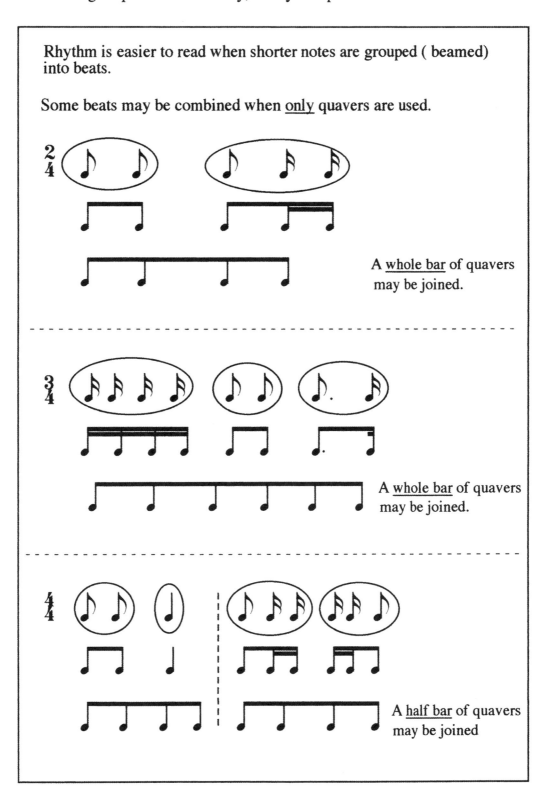

EXERCISES in GROUPING NOTES

Exercise 46 Draw circles to show how these notes make up crotchet beats. Then re-write each bar, joining quavers and semiquavers where necessary. The beginning of the first exercise has been done for you as a guide.

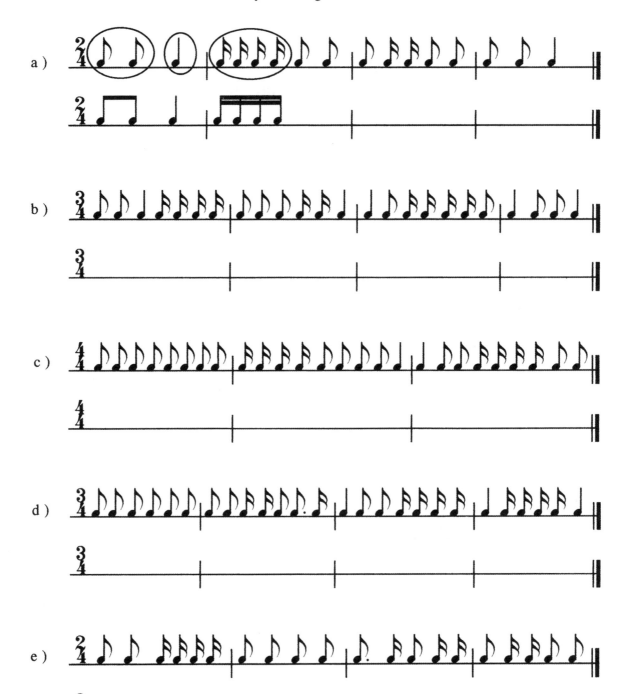

In this exercise, remember that the dot after a <u>crotchet</u> is part of the next beat.

SCALE of D MAJOR

Every major scale follows this pattern :

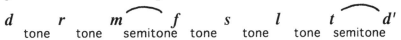

d *r* *m* *f* *s* *l* *t* *d'*
tone tone semitone tone tone tone semitone

If we use a keyboard drawing and follow this pattern of tone and semitone steps, we find the notes which will form a major scale starting with D.

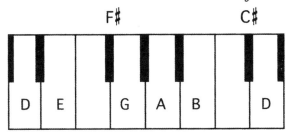

F♯ and C♯ are needed to put the semitone steps in the right place and so make the sound correct.

This is the scale of D major ascending and descending. The sharps are written before the notes as accidentals. Solfa names are added and semitones marked.

d *r* *m* *f* *s* *l* *t* *d'* *d'* *t* *l* *s* *f* *m* *r* *d*

Here is the scale of D major. The sharps are at the beginning as a key signature.

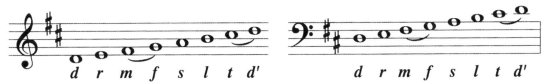

d *r* *m* *f* *s* *l* *t* *d'*   *d* *r* *m* *f* *s* *l* *t* *d'*

Exercise 47 a) Add a bass clef and accidentals to make this the scale of D major.

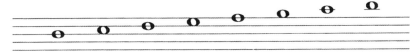

b) Add a clef and key signature to make this the scale of D major.

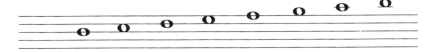

c) Add the key signature to make this the scale of D major. Write the solfa names below the notes and mark the semitones.

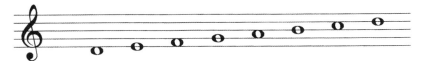

d) Write the scale of D major in <u>minims</u> descending. Use accidentals.

SINGING with SOLFA 5 : ADDING *fa*

●   In this group of tunes a new note *fa* (*f*) is added. It comes between *mi* and *so*. It is a half step (semitone) higher than *mi*.

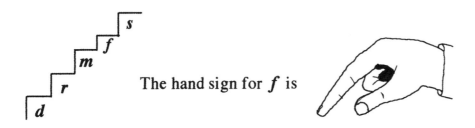

The hand sign for *f* is

Exercise 48   Sing each of these tunes using tonic solfa names. Keep an even beat by tapping quietly with your hand or foot.

a)
d r m r m f s m f s f m r d

b)
d r m f m f s m d

c)
d r d r m f m s f m f m r d

d)
d r m r m f s m f s m f s m r d

e)
d m s d r m f s s m d s f m r d

f)
d m f s s m r m d d

Exercise 49   Finish the tune by composing your own missing bar. When you have finished writing, sing the complete tune.

d r m f s m f s

SINGING with SOLFA 6 : *d r m f s* on the Stave

Here are *d* , *r* , *m* , *f* and *s* in the keys of C , G , and D major.

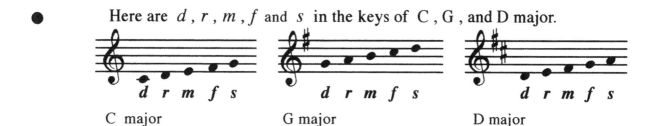

C major   G major   D major

Exercise 50 Sing each tune using tonic solfa names. Keep a steady beat while doing so.

Exercise 51 Finish the tune by composing your own missing bar. First, decide the rhythm and the solfa names you want to use, then write them on the stave. Sing the complete tune when you have finished writing.

GENERAL OBSERVATION 3

This is the right hand part of the opening of a piano piece by Haydn. Study the music. Then answer the questions below.

a) Give the meaning of these musical terms and signs.

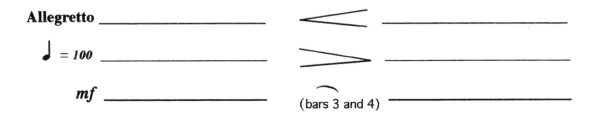

Allegretto _____   < _____

♩ = 100 _____   > _____

mf _____   ⌢ _____
(bars 3 and 4)

b) Fill in the blanks to complete each sentence.

The music is written in the key of ____ major. The rhythm of bar 3 is repeated

in bar ____ . Sixteenth notes are used in every bar except bar ____. The time

name of the longest note is a _____ _____ ; it lasts for

____ crotchet beats. The melody begins on *s* and ends on ____ .

c) To answer these questions, tick the box with the correct answer.

i) How many times is B heard ? | 1 | 2 | 3 |

ii) How many times is C♯ heard ? | 5 | 6 | 7 |

iii) Which of these bars has notes moving only by step ? | 4 | 5 | 6 |

iv) Of which bar is bar 5 a repeat ? | 1 | 2 | 3 |

v) How many semiquavers equal a dotted quaver ? | 2 | 3 | 4 |

TEST 3

Q. 1 In each box draw one dotted note equal to the value of each pair of notes.

  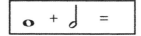 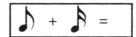

Q. 2 Add the missing bar lines in this rhythm.

Q. 3 a) Group these notes into crotchet beats by drawing circles as shown in bar 1.

b) Now re-write the rhythm joining quavers and semiquavers as necessary.

Q. 4 Add a clef sign and accidentals to make these notes form the scale of D major.

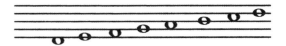

Q. 5 After the clef draw the key signature for D major. Write solfa names below; mark semitones.

Q. 6 Write this tune on the stave in the key of C major. The opening has been done for you.

Q. 7 Some signs have been left out in the next melody. Follow the directions and add in those signs which are needed.

i) Make the last 2 notes in bar 1 staccato.

ii) Show that the first three notes in bar 2 are to be played smoothly.

iii) Show that the last note in bar 2 should not be played sharp.

iv) Tie the last note in bar 3 to the first note in bar 4.

● The time signatures you have learnt so far are $\frac{2}{4}$, $\frac{3}{4}$ and $\frac{4}{4}$. All these are described as **simple** time signatures. Other words are also used when describing time signatures. For example :

The word **duple** means 2. So $\frac{2}{4}$ is described as being **simple duple** time.

The word **triple** means 3. So $\frac{3}{4}$ is described as being **simple triple** time.

The word **quadruple** means 4. So $\frac{4}{4}$ is described as being **simple quadruple** time.

Exercise 52 Add the time signature to each of the melodies below. In each case describe the time as ' simple duple ', ' simple triple ' or ' simple quadruple '.

In this group of clapping exercises tied crotchets are combined with paired quavers ♪♪, grouped semiquavers ♬♬, dotted crotchets and quavers ♩. ♪ and crotchet rests.

Exercise 53 Clap each of the following rhythms while keeping a steady beat.

a)

b)

c)

d)

e)

f)

g)

h)

i)

j)

RESTS in GROUPING

● Rhythm is easier to read when notes are grouped into beats. When rests are included we should still be able to follow the beats easily. To allow you to write rests correctly, study the following points.

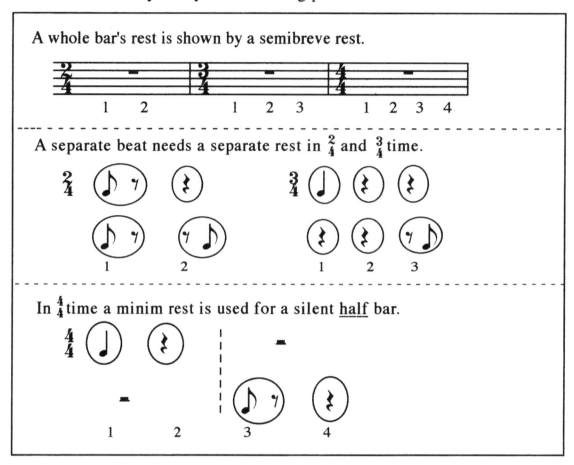

Exercise 54 Some bars are silent at places marked *. Draw in the missing rest or rests, taking care with the grouping.

● If you are not sure of the pattern of tone and semitone steps which form the major scale, go back to page 29 to revise it.

Now use this keyboard drawing to pick out a major scale starting from F .

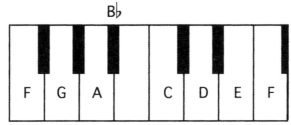

B♭ is needed to put the semitone step in the correct place.

This is the scale of F major ascending and descending. A flat is drawn before the note B as an accidental. Solfa names are added and the semitones are marked.

Here is the scale of F major with its B flat written as a key signature.

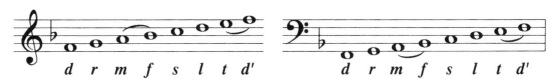

Exercise 55 Complete the following exercises.

a) Write the scale of F major ascending and descending in the bass clef. Use an accidental.

b) Add a clef and key signature to make this the scale of F major.

c) Add a clef and accidental to make this the scale of F major. Include the solfa names and mark the semitones.

d) Write the scale of F major with key signature. Write the scale ascending in minims. Mark the semitones.

SCALES / KEYS of C , G , D and F

●   This table shows a summary of the scales and their key signatures.

SCALE / KEY	KEY SIGNATURE	
C major	⸺	⸺
G major	1 sharp	F♯
D major	2 sharps	F♯ C♯
F major	1 flat	B♭

Exercise 56 Add accidentals before any notes needing them to form the named scales. Then write the solfa names beneath the notes and mark the semitones.

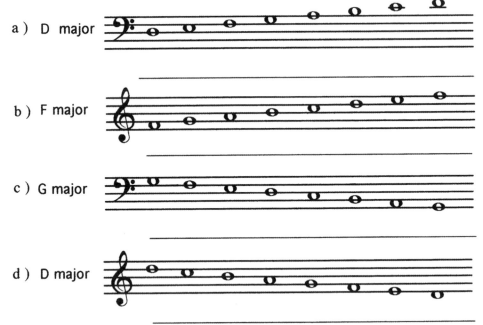

a) D major

b) F major

c) G major

d) D major

Exercise 57 Write each of these scales with its key signature.

a) G major ascending in crotchets

b) F major descending in minims.

c) D major ascending in semibreves.

Exercise 58 Name the key (scale) to which each key signature belongs.

ACCIDENTALS and KEYS : EXERCISES

Before you work these exercises, revise the points on page 18 about the use of accidentals.

Exercise 59 Add accidentals to suit the key named for each melody. Then write the solfa names below the notes in the first two bars in every case.

Exercise 60 Rewrite each of these melodies using accidentals instead of a key signature.

SINGING with SOLFA 7 : d r m f s l

Exercise 61 Sing each tune using tonic solfa names. Keep a steady beat by quietly tapping.

a) d r m f s l s s l s f m r d

b) d m f s l s m f m

c) d m s s l s s l s f m r d

d) d s l s m f m r d

e) m r d r m f f m s l s f m r r d

d r m f s l : in the Keys of C, G, D, F

Exercise 62 Sing each tune with solfa names. Keep a steady beat.

a) d

b) d

c) d

d) d

e) d

This is part of the traditional Irish melody called " *The Derry Air* ". It is arranged here for 'cello. Study the music. Then answer the questions below.

a) Give the meaning of these musical terms and signs.

Andante_____   ⟨   _____

grazioso_____   ⟩   _____

mf   _____   ♩ = 80   _____

b) 1. What is the other name for the bass clef ?   The _____ clef.

2. Name the key in which the music is written.   _____

3. For how many crotchet beats does the tied note in bar 3 last ? _____

4. For how many crotchet beats does the tied note in bar 5 last ? _____

5. Give the letter name of the lowest note. _____

6. How many quaver rests are in the melody ? _____

c) To answer these questions, tick the box with the correct answer.

1. The melody ends on ? | *do* | *re* | *mi* |

2. The melody begins on ? | *so* | *do* | *ti* |

3. The repeat of the opening starts in bar | 4 | 5 | 6 |

4. How many times is E played ? | 6 | 7 | 8 |

5. Which bar has notes moving only by step ? | 6 | 7 | 8 |

6. ⁴⁄₄ time is described as | duple | triple | quadruple |

TEST 4

Q.1 Write the numbers for each of these time signatures. Then fill one bar of each time with quavers, correctly grouped.

simple quadruple   simple duple   simple triple

Q.2 Write the scale of F major ascending in crotchets. Use an accidental instead of a key signature.

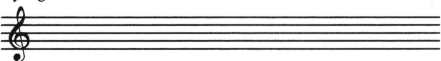

Q.3 Draw the key signature for each of these keys:

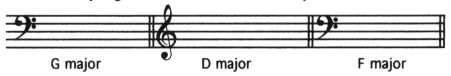

G major   D major   F major

Q.4 Draw the missing rest or rests where you see * . Take care with the grouping.

Q.5 Re-write this melody using accidentals instead of a key signature.

Q.6 Write this tune on the stave in the key of G major. Bar 1 is already done for you.

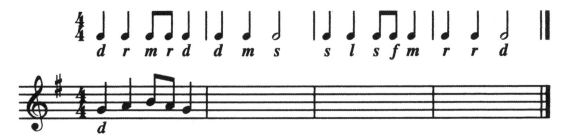

Q.7 After each of these notes write another note which is a tone higher.

DIRECTION of STEMS in GROUPING

●   The rules for the direction in which stems are drawn are the following;

1. Stems of all notes in a group need to be drawn in the same direction so that they may be easily joined. For example

2. The direction of the stems in a group is decided by the majority.

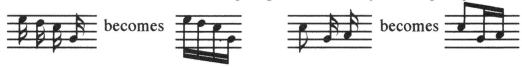

3. Suit the note furthest from the middle line, if the number of stems in each direction is equal.

Exercise 63 Draw circles to show how these notes make up crotchet beats. Rewrite the notes, changing the direction of any stems where necessary within the same group.

TONIC TRIAD

● **Tonic** is the name given to the first note of a scale. Other names for the first note are *do* and **keynote**.

The word **triad** means three.

A **tonic triad** is made up of three notes. They are the **first** note, the **third** note and the **fifth** note of a scale. In solfa, a tonic triad is made by *do*, *mi* and *so*.

This is the tonic triad of C at different pitches.

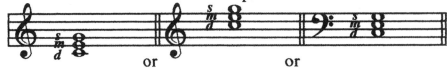

Exercise 64 Write the key signature and tonic triad of each of these keys.

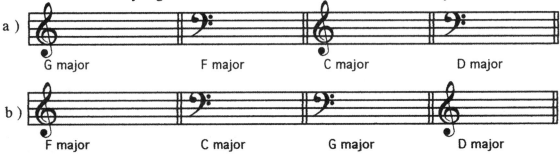

Exercise 65 Write the tonic triad of these keys. Use accidentals instead of key signature.

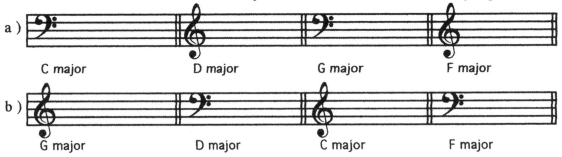

Exercise 66 Name the key to which each key signature belongs. Then write its tonic triad.

Exercise 67 Name the key of this melody. Find three places where the notes of the tonic triad follow one another. Draw a large circle round the notes of each tonic triad.

Key _____

MELODIES with ACCIDENTALS : NAMING the KEY

Exercise 68 Study the accidentals carefully in the following melodies. Then name the key of each melody.

a)
Mendelssohn. 'Christmas piece'

Key : _____

b)
Sullivan. 'Mikado'

Key : _____

c)
Beethoven. Piano sonata

Key : _____

d)
Mozart.'The Magic Flute'

Key : _____

e)
"Cherry Ripe"

Key : _____

f)
Strauss. 'The Bat'

Key : _____

g)
J.S.Bach. Prelude

Key : _____

h)
J.S.Bach. 2pt. Invention

Key : _____

i)
Schubert. 'Unfinished' Symphony'

Key : _____

SPECIAL ASSIGNMENT

You have learnt to sing *d r m f s l* and to read them in stick notation.
You have also learnt to read and write them on the stave in the keys of C, G,
D and F. Now compose your own 'missing bars ' in the next group of tunes.
Of course it is important to sing the tune first, so that you can hear which
notes and rhythm sound best in the missing bars. Sing each complete tune
when you have finished writing.

a)

Now write the whole tune on the stave below in the key of C major.

b)

Now write the whole tune on the stave below in the key of G major.

c)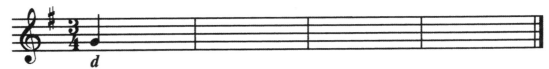

Now write the whole tune on the stave below in the key of D major.

These melodies are already written on the stave. Add the missing bar.

d)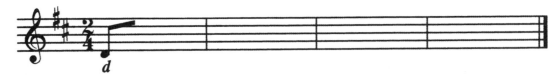

e)

f)

GENERAL OBSERVATION 5

This is an old English folksong " *Early one morning* ". Study the music. Then answer the questions below.

a) What terms or signs are shown on the music which have the following meanings?

fairly lively _____   play smoothly _____

gradually getting louder _____   gradually getting softer _____

play fairly softly _____   get slower just a little_____

b) Fill in the blanks to complete each sentence.

The melody is in the key of _____ major. $\frac{2}{4}$ means that there are ____ beats in

a bar and each beat is worth a _____. This time is described as

simple _____ time. The melody begins by repeating *d* , then in bar 2

it moves up from *d* to ___ and ___ . These notes form the tonic _____.

c) Tick the box to show whether the sentence is ' true' or ' false '.

   i) Bars 1 - 4 and bars 5 - 8 are fairly similar. | true | | false |

   ii) The lowest note is *d*. | true | | false |

   iii) Bars 14 - 16 contain part of a descending scale. | true | | false |

   iv) Bar 8 contains a full beat rest. | true | | false |

   v) Bars 9 and 10 are repeated immediately. | true | | false |

TEST 5

Q.1(a) Draw circles to show how these notes make up crotchet beats.

(b) Now rewrite the notes correctly grouped on the stave below. Change the direction of stems within the group where necessary.

Q.2 Name the keys of these tonic triads.

Q.3 Name the key of the following melody.

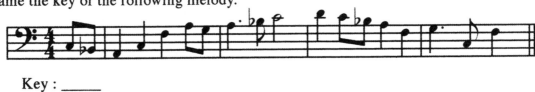

Key : _____

Q.4 Write the scale of G major in the bass clef with key signature. Write the scale ascending in minims. Mark the semitones.

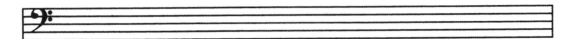

Q.5 Study the following melody. Then complete the questions which follow.

a) After the bass clef draw the key signature for D major.

b) Draw the necessary rest or rests to complete bar 1.

c) Circle two notes which are tied.

d) For how many crotchet beats does this tied sound last ?_____

e) Mark with ⌐‐‐⌐ three notes following one another which make up the tonic triad of D major.

f) Explain ♩=100 _____

g) Is ♩=100 a fast or a slow tempo ?_____

h) Does the time signature mean duple, triple or quadruple time ? _____

▦ Tempo and Changes of Tempo

accelerando	gradually getting faster	Largo	slow
a tempo	back to normal speed	Moderato	moderate speed
Adagio	slow	M.M. ♩ = *60*	60 crotchet beats per minute
Allegretto	fairly quick and lively	rall. (rallentando)	gradually getting slower
Allegro	quick and lively	ritard.(ritardando)	gradually getting slower
Andante	walking speed	rit. (ritenuto)	gradually getting slower

▦ Dynamics

f	*forte*	loud	*p*	*piano*	soft
ff	*fortissimo*	very loud	*pp*	*pianissimo*	very soft
mf	*mezzo forte*	moderately loud	*mp*	*mezzo piano*	moderately soft
	cresc.	gradually getting louder		dim.	gradually getting softer
				decresc.	gradually getting softer

▦ Articulation

Legato	play smoothly		–	stress
Staccato	play detached		>	accent

▦ Style

dolce	sweetly
grazioso	gracefully
cantabile	singing style

▦ Signs

⌢	pause
8*va* – – – – – ˌ	Play one octave higher
8*vb* – – – – – ˌ	Play one octave lower
⫶‖	Repeat
⫶‖⫶	Repeat the sections before and after

1	2		
	‖	‖	On 1st playing, play bar 1. Play bar 2 after the repeat

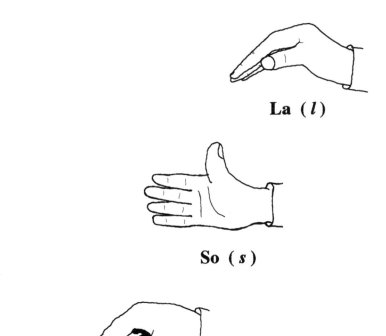

La (*l*)

So (*s*)

Fa (*f*)

Mi (*m*)

Re (*r*)

Do (*d*)

HOMEWORK RECORD

DATE	WRITTEN EXERCISE Exercise number	CLAPPING / SINGING EXERCISE Exercise number	TEACHER COMMENT